THE GIFT OF
LAUGHTER

NANCY GOUDIE

First Edition 2014 ISBN 978-0-9564512-3-1

Concept design by Ray Goudie and Nancy Goudie

Graphic design by Lewis Royal

Illustrations by Alex McGinn

Published by New Generation Music,
Caedmon Complex,
Bristol Road,
Thornbury,
Bristol,
BS35 3JA,
UK

www.ngm.org.uk

Print management by Verité CM Ltd
www.veritecm.com

THE GIFT OF
LAUGHTER

PROLOGUE

Imagine the scene! Ray my husband, Daniel our son (who was about four at the time) and myself were on holiday in Majorca. The three of us were staying in a small apartment in Santa Ponsa – the sun was shining and each of us was eager to spend some time in the sun. Daniel kept hurrying us to get our swimwear on so that he could enjoy the pool. When we eventually arrived at the pool, we found three sun loungers, put our towels on them and lay down to enjoy some time resting and relaxing, but Daniel was eager to get in the pool and he wanted his dad to go with him. Ray said he would go into the pool shortly and asked Daniel to wait ten minutes, but like all young children, he couldn't wait. He kept pestering his dad and Ray kept repeating the same thing, *"Give me ten minutes Daniel"*.

Eventually Daniel got frustrated and annoyed with his

dad and said, *"You haven't even got your swim shorts on anyway!"* Ray and I looked at each other with shocked expressions and then looked to see what Ray was wearing. We discovered that he had walked down several flights of stairs to the pool in his underpants. There he was in all his glory lying flat out in his brilliant white Calvin Klein Y Fronts! I burst out laughing while Ray scrambled to try and hide his pants! He panicked and said, *"What am I going to do?"*

I said, *"You walked down here in your pants, so you are just going to have to walk back up to the apartment in them!"* Daniel and I laughed and laughed!

LAUGHTER IS LIKE AN INSTANT VACATION

Laughter has a way of changing the atmosphere and instead of conflict it creates joy! It is an incredible gift given to help us live life to the full. Laughter releases joy and causes our souls to dance with delight, but it also brings so much more.

During this book I will outline a few of the amazing benefits that I have discovered that laughter brings. I will also be sharing many interesting quotes, as well as many funny stories to help you ignite the laughter within. So many good things happen when we laugh. Did you know that laughter can help us lose weight, lift our mood, it can relax us and believe it or not even smooth our wrinkles, whilst at the same time improve our health in so many ways? When we laugh it can make us feel as though we have been on an instant vacation, which is maybe why many good comedians are finding that their audiences are growing so fast these days. People love to laugh – it makes them feel good!

We live in an exhausting world often full of stress, concern and worry; I believe that one of the answers we need to combat these difficulties is laughter. Experts tell us that just 15 minutes of laughter can give the same benefit as two hours of sleep. People have discovered that a diet of reading funny stories and watching comedy films that make you laugh can have a significant effect on their physical health. It has been said that one good belly laugh burns off 3 to 4 calories and that laughing only 15 seconds can add two days to your life span!

Each of us has been created with the ability to laugh. I am sure you will find it interesting to note that research tells us that the part of the brain that facilitates laughter is among the first parts of the nervous system to come on line after birth. You will discover as you read this book what an incredible gift it is as we explore its many benefits. Perhaps the biggest benefit of laughter is that you don't have to pay to receive it - it's a free gift! You already have the language of laughter within you and it has no negative side affects! Isn't that wonderful? Use it and it could increase your quality and even your quantity of life.

If you are looking for a book that has an in depth study on laughter, then you will need to look elsewhere for this type of information. This is not that kind of book. However, if you are looking for tips, bite sized pieces of interesting information, interesting quotes on laughter and stories to help you laugh then this is the book for you. Most pages have laughter stories that have either happened to me or to someone I know. These stories come from every day situations – some are funny and some are laugh out loud funny! This book is similar in style to my popular series of books called 'The Beloved', 'Confident?' and 'You are Special' in that it is designed in such a way that if you open it at any page you will find something either to make you laugh and giggle or something to encourage or inspire you about laughter.

As someone who has a Christian faith, I do believe that God created laughter and gave it to us as a gift. I believe he made us in his image and therefore he too is a happy God who laughs! However, whether you believe in a God, have a vibrant faith, or whether you have no faith at all, I am convinced that this book can enable you to use this wonderful gift of laughter. So come with me as we...laugh out loud.

LAUGHING AT YOUR
OWN MISTAKES CAN
LENGTHEN YOUR LIFE.

LAUGHING AT YOUR
WIFE'S MISTAKES CAN
SHORTEN IT!

SHE'S AWFUL

A man sat in a concert hall listening to a lady singing on the stage, but this lady's voice was not very tuneful in fact she was very out of tune. After a while, the man could not stand it any longer and turned to the man sitting next to him and said, *"Oh I can't stand this any longer. She's awful."*

The man next to him immediately answered and said, *"She's my wife."*

In his embarrassment, the first man tried to make things better by saying, *"Oh no I didn't mean she was awful, I meant the song was awful. If she had a good song, she would be really good."*

The man hesitated for a moment and then said, *"Actually, I wrote the song!"*

LAUGHTER RELAXES OUR MUSCLES!

In fact we cannot even smile never mind laugh without our bodies relaxing! Try it and you will discover this to be true. A good hearty laugh will relieve stress and tension and will leave your body relaxed for up to 45 minutes! As well as this, it's so good to know, as I said in my introduction that laughter even helps reduce wrinkles.

MISTAKEN
IDENTITY

During the 1980's my husband and I formed a band called Heartbeat, which travelled to various towns, cities and even nations to play our gigs. We had been invited to play at a festival in the summer and so we found ourselves sitting in a caravan chatting about our concert. Just before leaving the caravan to go on stage we decided to pray together. Within the band we had two couples Ian and Dorry, Ray and myself and two single people – Dave and Trish. When we started to pray Dave began to get increasingly worried. During the prayer, Ian decided to take Dorry's hand and caress it, but because his eyes were shut, he didn't realise that instead of stroking Dorry's hand, he was lovingly stroking Dave's hand! We could not stop laughing when we discovered what had happened!

A DAY WITHOUT LAUGHTER IS A DAY WASTED

CHARLIE CHAPLIN

WANDERING
MINSTREL

A friend of ours who is a singer/songwriter was on side stage ready to perform at a gig when he decided he needed to visit the toilet. He thought he had enough time to get there and back before he was announced from stage, however, he forgot that he had an open microphone attached to him. The whole audience heard more from him that day than they had thought they would!

At another gig, our friend left the stage to loud applause as people cheered not only for his performance but also for the band who were playing the second half of the show. He exited through a stage door to discover rather than being behind stage, he had mistakenly entered a broom cupboard and could not get out until the second half of the show was over!

LAUGHTER BOOSTS THE IMMUNE SYSTEM!

Laughter triggers the release of an anti-body called immunoglobulin, which boosts the immune system and produces a general sense of well-being. According to clinical studies laughter has shown that it clearly strengthens the immune system. So laugh your way to good health!

THE CHRISTMAS
TOOTHBRUSH

The presents were all wrapped, the Santa sacks filled with all sorts of goodies, the turkey was ready to go on in the morning. Christmas for me has always been a day filled with joy! I have so many childhood memories of waking up at some unearthly hour on Christmas morning with my younger brother and eagerly opening our presents! The look on our faces must have matched what I saw when my own children opened their presents, the anticipation, the amazement and of course the joy! There is much joy in not only receiving but in giving!

I remember my son, Daniel once asking us what we had bought him for Christmas! I immediately answered, *"Oh this year we have bought you a toothbrush!"* He looked at our faces and immediately knew we were teasing him but we laughed as we jokingly insisted that it was true! The next day we laughed even more when he opened a gift to find someone had actually given him a toothbrush! His face was a picture of complete bewilderment! We had no idea this person was planning to give him a toothbrush!

LAUGHTER IS
THE SUN THAT
DRIVES WINTER FROM
THE HUMAN FACE

VICTOR HUGO

NO NEED TO
KNOCK

A number of years ago Ray and I were playing/singing in a band at a festival in the northeast of England. Two of our friends who were husband and wife were also performing at the same festival. I happened to mention that I had forgotten to bring a hairdryer with me and the wife said I could borrow hers whenever I wanted. I said I would wash my hair and come straight over to their apartment. After washing my hair, Ray and I walked over to where they were staying. They had told me just to walk straight in and so that is what I did. As I pushed the door open, Ray quickly said, *"Should you not knock and wait"*. I confidently said, *"No she told me to walk straight in."* As we walked in through the door, we saw two naked bodies sliding down the side of the bed to hide from us. They were laughing like crazy with embarrassment as we said, *"Oops we will come back later – we only wanted the hairdryer!"*

LAUGHTER DECREASES PAIN

Experts tell us that 10 minutes of laughter can result in two hours of pain relief. Laughter can help us to forget our aches and pains, even pain from arthritis!

A STIFF DRINK

I heard a story the other day from a friend whose mum sadly died in a car crash in the year 2000. When someone informed her sister that her Mum had died, as you can imagine she was devastated at the news and told her fiancé that she needed a stiff drink. She asked him for whatever they had in the house. He went off into the kitchen and a few minutes later she heard the popping of a champagne cork; he swears it was the only alcohol in the house!

A GOOD LAUGH
AND A LONG SLEEP
ARE THE BEST CURES
IN THE DOCTOR'S BOOK

IRISH PROVERB

WHERE'S MY SHIRT?

My husband couldn't find his best white shirt! He doesn't often get lots of opportunities to wear a shirt, but this was the second time in as many days that he'd had an engagement that required him to wear his white shirt. He hunted for it everywhere telling me that he put it in the washing basket so that it could be washed overnight. I hunted everywhere with him and we couldn't find it. We eventually discovered that he had not put it in the washing basket, but had instead thrown it into the waste paper basket! His best shirt was on its way to the rubbish tip and there was no way to get it back! That's when I thought my husband was definitely getting old! It was a bit of a disaster, but it did make us laugh!

LAUGHTER LOWERS BLOOD PRESSURE

Stress is one of the biggest contributors to high blood pressure and laughter is a brilliant antidote to stress. Studies have shown that only ten minutes of laughter can reduce blood pressure by 10-20 mm. When people have a good laugh initially their blood pressure will increase but then it lowers to levels below normal.

YOU'VE GOT TO
LAUGH!

A number of years ago Ray and I had the privilege of meeting and getting to know a man who was a personal chaplain to the Queen. He came to our offices because he wanted to find out more about our work. He was a very interesting and intriguing man and we got on like a house on fire! At the end of our conversation, he and Ray swapped personal phone numbers and then he left. Later on that day, Ray was at the hairdressers when he had a phone call from the same man asking if he could meet Ray again. He was in the High Street of our town, just further up the road. So Ray went to meet him. I was to meet Ray at the hairdressers but of course when I arrived to pick him up in our car, he had gone. The hairdresser told me that Ray had gone to meet the Queen's personal chaplain. I explained that this could not be right, as we had met him that morning. He said with a shrug, *"Oh I don't know then, maybe he has gone to meet the Queen!"* I laughed and went looking for Ray! I found him further up the High Street with our new friend. He told me to go on home and he would get dropped off later. I went to our local supermarket, which was on the way home.

The first thing I saw when I arrived back at our home was that Ray was sitting in a vehicle outside our house talking to the Queen's personal chaplain and his assistant. I debated with myself, shall I go and say hello, knowing that I would have to invite him and his assistant into our home or should I just leave it and check the house first. I couldn't remember how I had left the house that morning and after all this was a personal chaplain to the Queen! So, I went into the house and quickly tidied it up just in case Ray decided to ask him in. I put all the rubbish I could find into the utility room at the back door and looked around the lounge and thought it looked reasonable. I had just convinced myself that Ray would not invite him to come in, when I heard the door open! I went to invite them in, but then realised that Ray was bringing them in through the back door, past all the rubbish I had put in there, past all the dirty washing and the ironing into the kitchen! This is the Queen's personal chaplain and Ray brought him in through the back door! I could not believe it – I mean, what is it about men?!!

I quickly ushered them into the lounge praying that they had temporarily lost their ability to see! After providing them with a drink, I sat in the lounge congratulating myself that I had tidied the house before Ray brought them in, when all of a sudden my eyes were opened! I could not believe it! How did I miss them? Right next to the Queen's personal chaplain, drying over the radiator, were two pairs of Ray's underpants!

I AM NOT HERE TO
ENTERTAIN YOU.
I AM HERE TO
MAKE YOU LAUGH AT
THE IMPOSSIBLE!

SMITH WIGGLESWORTH

A SLAP IN THE FACE!

When I was a young girl, my brother Tom, who is eight years older than me, was dating a lovely girl called Elaine. She eventually became his wife, but it could have worked out so differently had she not been so forgiving. One night, she stayed at our home but because my parents ran a hotel, all our spare rooms were fully booked with guests so she shared a double bed with me. In the middle of the night, I sat up in bed and shouted, *"Shut up, Jack"*, then slapped Elaine across the face before promptly falling asleep again! I have no recollection of doing this even to this day, however, I do remember dreaming that I had an argument with Jack, my younger brother, and he so annoyed me that I slapped him across the face! Elaine said she wanted to retaliate but there was nothing she could do because by the time she realised what had happened, I had fallen fast asleep with an angelic look on my face!

LAUGHTER MASSAGES THE HEART

(as well as other vital organs in our body) and can help prevent heart disease and heart attacks.

HOW
EMBARRASSING!

A friend shared this story with me when they realised I was writing a book on laughter.

"A few years ago a hard-working and well-respected young man in our church, who had recently got married, suddenly and entirely unexpectedly dropped dead of a heart attack. I attended the funeral but arrived a little late and so missed any request there might have been for mobile phones to be switched off. During the quietest part of the service (of course) - the address - my mobile phone rang. What was worse, in my embarrassment I couldn't find it quickly and so the tune played two or three times before I was able to silence it. The tune? 'Wish me luck as you wave me goodbye'!"

THROUGH HUMOUR,
YOU CAN SOFTEN SOME
OF THE WORST BLOWS
THAT LIFE DELIVERS.
AND ONCE YOU FIND
LAUGHTER, NO MATTER
HOW PAINFUL YOUR
SITUATION MIGHT BE,
YOU CAN SURVIVE IT

BILL CROSBY

THE NAKED CHEF

In the 80's my husband Ray and I used to travel extensively throughout Britain and Europe with our band. In those days when we visited an area the organiser would often arrange for us to stay in people's homes rather than put us in a hotel. The people who gave us hospitality were often people we had never met before.

One evening, two of our band members who are married arrived at their host's house and throughout the hour or so before going to bed received instructions about the morning. The hosts very kindly told our fellow musicians that they should treat the house as though it was their own and told them to help themselves to breakfast the following morning as they would be leaving very early.

In the morning when our friends heard their hosts leave the house, the husband decided to go to the kitchen to get some breakfast. As he usually slept with nothing on and as his host had encouraged him to treat the house like his own, he went downstairs into the kitchen naked. He was getting breakfast ready to take upstairs when he heard the front door being opened with a key. As you can imagine, he panicked! His confidence at walking around the house with nothing on suddenly disappeared! He ran into the walk-in larder and closed the door and prayed like crazy that the host would not open the larder door. Fortunately the host only came back for something he had forgotten and then left!

LAUGHTER IS AN EXCELLENT AEROBIC EXERCISE.

Laughing 100 times is as much a workout as 10 minutes of rowing or 15 minutes on an exercise bike.

OUT OF THE
MOUTH OF BABES

One particular Sunday, children from a local Sunday school were performing and reading in a church service for all the adult church members. A young couple was overheard telling their child, *"If you are really good and do well and read your lines properly, we can go to KFC for lunch."* As the vicar was nearing the end of his discussion about the destinations of good versus evil he proclaimed *"and we all know where people who behave well go, don't we?"* Without a moment's hesitation, this young chap shouted out, *"I do! They go to KFC!!!"*

LAUGHTER
IS INFECTIOUS

GOD IS
WATCHING YOU

I heard a story recently about a Catholic school run by nuns. As the children were queuing to get their lunch they noticed a bowl of apples with a sign on it saying, *'Take one apple only – God is watching you!'* Further along the line, there were a plate of chocolate chip cookies and one of the children had written a note on it saying, *'Take as many as you want, God is watching the apples!'*

LAUGHTER HELPS YOU LOSE WEIGHT!

Researchers at Vanderbilt University found 10 - 15 minutes of laughter burns off around 40 calories. According to research a healthy laugh a day could burn 2 to 4 pounds of fat, even without changing your dietary habits. Sounds good to me!

THE MISSING
FALSE TEETH

All was quiet in the library as a little grey haired old man approached the counter.

"Good morning sir, how can I help you," said Dawn the librarian.

"I've lost my teeth!" came the strange reply.

Dawn could see that it was indeed true as his mouth appeared very sunken without the said teeth. She tried hard to disguise her smile as she replied, *"Your teeth, sir?"*

"Yes my teeth – can you find them for me?"

At this the other librarians started to giggle and Dawn fought very hard to keep from laughing herself. She replied with a straight face, *"I'm so sorry you have lost your teeth sir. I have to say it is normally umbrellas or even children that people seem to lose. I have never had a lost set of teeth before!"*

At this point the other people in the library were beginning to listen to the conversation and were starting to laugh too.

"They are new and I cannot leave without them," he replied.

"I can assure you sir, we will try and locate your teeth for you! Where did you lose them sir and why did you remove them?"

By this time everyone in listening distance was finding it difficult to conceal the laughter that was rising inside.

"Well, I was in the crime section, and I took my teeth out to read a book."

At this, there was a loud explosion of laughter from around the library! Everyone including Dawn and even the old man himself were laughing loudly! He said he found it easier to read the book without his teeth!

In the end they couldn't find the teeth, but a few days later a woman returned them to the library. It turned out that when the man took his teeth out they had somehow fallen into the woman's shopping bag and she had found them when she next went shopping!

YOU DON'T STOP LAUGHING
WHEN YOU GROW OLD;
YOU GROW OLD WHEN
YOU STOP LAUGHING.

GEORGE BERNARD SHAW

THIS IS A
BORING SONG

It was in the 80's and our band, Heartbeat, was in the middle of a concert. In the venue were hundreds of teenagers who had seen us in their school that week. They had enjoyed what we did and had come to see us perform at a local theatre. The band was loud but it seemed like the audience were even louder at times as they whistled and cheered through the songs. In the middle of the set, we had asked Dorry, one of our singers, to perform a beautiful slow ballad. She has an amazing voice and really suited this type of song. She hadn't been sure about performing this song to this audience, but Ray and I persuaded her that the audience would love it. The audience grew quiet as the song progressed but then one girl, who was standing right at the front of stage, turned to her friend and shouted, *"This is a boring song!"* I am sure the comment didn't do much to increase Dorry's confidence, but later both she and the rest of us in the band howled with laughter.

LAUGHTER RELIEVES STRESS

Experts have discovered that laughter can reduce stress hormones that constrict blood vessels and suppress immune activity. Laughter is such a brilliant way to release stress in each of us.

IT'S TIME TO
GET UP, RAY

I woke up one morning at 6.00am, put the light on at my side of the bed and picked up my journal and Bible. I wrote in my book amongst other things, *"Lord, thank you for a good night's rest"* before going on to read my Bible. As Ray began to stir, he kept saying, *"I cannot get my eyes open, Nancy! I don't know what is wrong with me. I'm so sleepy!"*

About 40 minutes later when Ray was fully awake and beginning to write in his own journal, I thought I had better see if it was time to wake my 14-year-old son Aidan, so that he could get ready for school. I looked at the clock on my phone to discover it was 2.30 in the morning! I could not believe it! What a mistake to make! I even thought I had remembered turning off the alarm! Ray was so relieved he turned over and promptly went back to sleep, but I couldn't stop chuckling to myself all night after that! It was so bizarre!

I'm sure someone somewhere will have some psychological explanation as to why I woke up at 2.30am thinking it was a number of hours later and why a few weeks later I almost did the same thing again! This time as I reached for the light switch, I put my brain into gear and thought I had better check that it was 6.00am. When I looked at my phone to see the time, I discovered it was only 1.15am! Ray had a lucky escape that time!

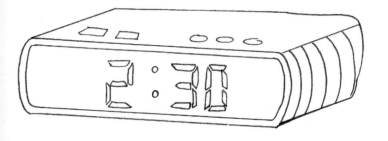

DON'T BE SO INTENSE;
INSTEAD ALWAYS
MAKE TIME TO LAUGH.

LAUGHTER NOT ONLY
ADDS YEARS TO YOUR LIFE,
BUT ADDS LIFE
TO YOUR YEARS!

TOO POLITE

We have collected many funny stories as we have travelled around the UK and beyond particularly in the 80's with our band Heartbeat. I remember staying in a very large home in Guildford with a really nice host. As it was the winter she asked me if I wanted a hot water bottle to heat up my bed. Normally I would have said, *"Yes"*, but because I was embarrassed I said, *"No thank you!"* As I walked up the stairs to the bedroom, I remembered I had my own hot water bottle with me as I was often cold in bed at night, so I thought I would fill it with hot water from the tap without my host knowing. In the morning, we left and it was only much later that I realized that I had left my hot water bottle in the bed!

LAUGHING YOUR WAY TO EMOTIONAL HEALTH

LAUGHTER ADDS STRENGTH AND ZEST TO LIFE

Many of us complain of being tired but maybe the answer is that we need to laugh a lot more often. You might be interested to know that experts tell us that 15 minutes of laughter equals the benefit of two hours of sleep, so when you are exhausted physically and emotionally – laugh a lot and you will find yourself refreshed!

DEAF IN BOTH EYES!

When my husband Ray said his first words on stage he got it all wrong. All he had to say was *"Hello, I am Ray from Prestwick."* However, because he was very nervous what came out was *"Hello, I'm Prestwick from Ray!"* A friend who worked in a bank did something quite similar. She introduced herself on stage by saying, *"Hi, I'm Christine and I'm a bank!"* When you are lacking in confidence sometimes words just don't come out the way they should!

A number of years later one of our band members who had not spoken much from stage went to the microphone and said, *"God has told me that there is someone here tonight who is deaf in both eyes and God wants to heal you. So if you are deaf in both eyes please come to the front and I will pray for you."* When he came off stage he could not understand why the rest of us were doubled over with laughter.

My husband was not put off by his first gaffe and has become an experienced public speaker over the years. However, a few years ago he made another mistake when he was speaking at a large church in Bristol. He told the audience that we should watch the screen as we were going to watch a film on VD! Amidst the laughter that followed he had to explain that what he meant to say was we were going to watch a film on DVD!!

WHY BE SERIOUS
ALL THE TIME WHEN
YOU CAN BE HAPPY
WITH LAUGHTER.

THE
YOUNG ARTIST

When one of our sons was young, we left him and his brother in the care of two friends while we had a couple of days away by ourselves. This couple didn't have any children themselves at the time and when we called home to ask how they were getting on they told us that they had had an interesting time with our youngest son.

They put him in bed for an afternoon nap and sometime later decided to go and see if he was awake. They said that as soon as they opened the door, the smell that hit them was so overpowering but what they saw shocked them completely! Our son had somehow managed to take off his dirty nappy and then proceeded to paint the cot with its contents! Not satisfied with that, he decided that he would plaster it on his head, his body and even in his mouth! Ray and I didn't know whether to laugh or die with embarrassment – we did both!

LAUGHTER EASES ANXIETY AND FEAR.

Laughter dissolves anxiety and fear - you cannot be anxious when you are laughing! Try it and see!

WOULD YOU LIKE
MORE WINE, SIR?

We had been invited on holiday by our special friends, John and Rose Lancaster and so together with our son Daniel and their son and daughter Steven and Julie, we went to a wonderful hotel in the Lake District. One evening John booked a table for us all in the best restaurant in the hotel. The meal was fantastic and we were thoroughly enjoying ourselves when Ray noticed that a couple who were sitting close to us had left the restaurant and had left almost a full bottle of red wine on their table. For fun, Ray got up and took a hold of their bottle of wine, put a napkin over his arm and pretended to be the waiter for our table. He poured some of the wine into Steven's glass saying, *"More wine, Sir?"* He then put the wine back and walked back to his chair.

Everyone at our table was laughing at Ray's antics, but what happened next had us literally underneath the table laughing out loud. As Ray sat down at our table, the couple whose wine Ray had taken walked back into the restaurant. They had not left the restaurant after all; they had only gone out for a smoke! They sat down at the table unaware that Ray had just poured about half a glass of their wine into Steven's glass. We laughed so much that within a few minutes the whole restaurant started laughing with us including the couple from the next table! What made it even funnier was that this couple and others in the restaurant asked, *"What are you laughing about?"* but there was no way we could have told them. We were still laughing hours later!

BLESSED ARE THOSE
WHO CAN LAUGH AT
THEMSELVES – FOR
THEY SHALL NEVER
CEASE TO BE AMUSED!

SO HAVE I!

A man decided to wallpaper a small bedroom in his home and knowing that his neighbour had recently done this he went to him for advice.

"How many rolls of wallpaper did you buy to do your spare bedroom", he asked.

His neighbour replied, *"I bought six"*.

The man thanked him and duly went and bought six. When he finished the room he had two rolls of wallpaper left. The next time he saw his neighbour he said to him, *"I bought six rolls of wallpaper and decorated my spare bedroom, but I have two rolls left."*

The neighbour replied, *"Yes – so have I."*

LAUGHTER IMPROVES YOUR MOOD.

Laughter is an instant mood improver as it's impossible to be sad or angry when laughter takes over!

THE CHINA POTTY

A few years ago I heard a true story about a male speaker who had been given overnight accommodation at a host's house. The host on this occasion was quite elderly and very nervous and so she explained to the orator that when he went to bed she would lock him in his room. She told him that if he needed to go to the toilet in the night, that she had put a china potty underneath the bed for his use. He never usually needed to go to the loo in the night, but of course what happened was that he needed to go that night. He tried as much as he could to hold it in, but eventually he had to make use of the china potty underneath the bed. In the morning he was embarrassed to walk with the potty to the bathroom to empty it and so he decided he would open the window and pour it out. As he held it upside down out of the upstairs window, the china potty somehow became detached from its handle and smashed onto the concrete garden path below. He was left with only the handle in his hand. How do you explain that to your host?

LAUGHTER IS THE KEY
TO A HEALTHY LIFE.

EXPOSED

A man was sitting at a table with a crowd of male and female peers when he noticed that his fly was undone. He was immediately embarrassed and so thought he would try to do the zip up without anyone noticing. In his mind he gave himself a pat on the back when he had completed this task without anyone noticing. Later as he walked away from the table he dragged the tablecloth with him causing all the crockery on the table to smash onto the floor! In his embarrassment and rush he had attached the tablecloth to the zip in his trousers!

LAUGHTER ENHANCES EMOTIONAL RESILIENCE

It releases stress and eases fear and anxiety. When we are faced with a difficult situation, if we use humour we can bounce back quicker!

A CHILD SPEAKS

I always think children can say the funniest things. I found a little boy's prayer recently on the Internet – it went like this: -

"Dear God, please take care of my daddy and my mummy and my sister and my brother and my doggy and my cat and me. Oh and please take care of yourself God because if anything happens to you, we're gonna be in a big mess."

And a story of a little girl saying grace...

A woman invited some people to dinner. At the table, she turned to her six-year-old daughter and said, *"Would you like to say the blessing on the food."*

"I wouldn't know what to say," the little girl replied.

"Just say what you hear Mummy say," the mother said.

The little girl bowed her head and said, *"Dear Lord, why on earth did I invite all these people to dinner?"*

LAUGHTER IS A MEDICINE
WITH NO SIDE EFFECTS

THE LOST SHOE

Zoe Wickham, a good friend of mine and also the General Manager of ngm was on a two-day course in London where she had to wear a proper business skirt and shoes. She got onto the tube at Paddington during rush hour when it was very busy but, as she stepped onto the train, she felt something brush her foot. As the doors closed she looked down to discover one of her shoes had fallen onto the track and she was now wearing only one shoe! As you can imagine she panicked as she had no other shoes with her and at 8am she knew most of the shops would be closed. This was her first time on a course with the Institute of Directors and she knew she couldn't show up without shoes! One girl on the train suggested she should go back and ask if they could get her shoe off the track. So at the next stop she got off and got some strange looks as she got on the next train back to Paddington with no shoes on her feet and one shoe in her hand! By this time she was on the verge of tears.

She went to see the supervisor who told her they didn't

normally stop trains in rush hour, however, as she could see how upset she was she said she would ask her boss. At this point, Zoe said she had never prayed so hard! After what felt like a long time they agreed they would stop the train. They made an announcement to the passengers on the platform saying that they were going to stop the train because someone had lost their shoe on the track. It seemed at that point that everyone turned and looked at Zoe. Her face was bright red, but she got her shoe!

When she got to her hotel that evening to check in, a man approached her and asked, *"Were you the one who lost a shoe on the underground this morning?"* Of all the millions of people in London, she could not believe she had bumped into someone who had seen her dilemma!

LAUGHTER STRENGTHENS RELATIONSHIPS

When family or friends watch a funny film, share a hilarious moment or tell a very good joke, it releases positive emotions that help us develop good relationships. Laughing with each other creates a bond between us and this will help in terms of any future disagreements or problems.

WHAT'S YOUR SECRET?

A doctor on his morning walk noticed an old deeply wrinkled lady. She was sitting on her front step smoking a cigar, so he walked up to her and said, *"I couldn't help but notice how happy you look! What's your secret?"*

"I smoke ten cigars a day," she said. *"Before I go to bed, I smoke a nice big joint. Apart from that, I drink a whole bottle of Jack Daniels every week and eat only junk food. On weekends I pop pills, have sex and I don't exercise at all."*

"That's absolutely amazing," he said. *"How old are you?"*

"Forty," she replied.

LAUGHTER IS
AN INSTANT VACATION

MILTON BERIE

IF YOU'VE GOT TO GO,
YOU'VE GOT TO GO!

A really funny and embarrassing incident happened to my husband Ray – here he is telling his own story!

A number of years ago when I was the drummer in the band Heartbeat we were asked to perform in a very old church. We were rehearsing in the afternoon when I suddenly had a severe sore stomach and knew I had to find a toilet as soon as possible!

I remember going to one of the young vergers in this very old Church of England building who told me, *"I'm sorry there are no toilets in the church!"* I think he took pity on me when he saw the total look of horror on my face. He said that the Vicar had a private toilet in his vestry and that he was sure he wouldn't mind me using it in an emergency. I went down these small winding stairs and found myself in a small room filled with vicars, church leaders and even a Canon. I then discovered that the toilet was a very small room only separated from the room they were all meeting in by a sliding door that didn't fully shut!

I somehow managed to squeeze myself onto the toilet and I just knew this was going to be totally embarrassing! No soundproofing, door not shutting and I felt I was sitting in the middle of the room with all these dignitaries! I had this picture in my mind of a cartoon where a smell is shown as a cloud in the shape of a pair of hands wafting across the room slapping all these vicars across the face! After the explosion and all the wonderful sound effects and me sitting there trying not to die with embarrassment, I then find out that the toilet paper was not the silent, nice, soft tissues but the hard, noisy, crinkly type! I don't how long I waited to pluck up enough courage to go back out and walk through the room and back upstairs but it seemed to take forever! I can still see their faces now!

LAUGHTER ATTRACTS OTHERS TO US

Laughter is like a magnet that draws people to you. When we hear laughter we are naturally drawn to the source of that laughter. Humour is also infectious; when one person laughs it can easily spread to others around.

THE
GARLIC PUDDING

Recently I was visiting a radio and television company with my husband Ray and friend Zoe to discuss a partnership between them and us. They very kindly gave us lunch whilst we discussed the possibilities of working together. When we finished our main course, they brought a pudding to us all. I politely asked what the pudding was called as it looked quite unusual and they replied, *"I believe its an apple something or other."*

I was looking forward to this 'apple something or other' especially since one of the others at the table had drenched each pudding in lots of single cream. As I took my first big bite, the taste hit me! It was disgusting! It had the most awful taste – I thought I was going to be sick! I knew there was no way I could eat anymore, but I didn't want to appear rude. I looked around to see if anyone else thought this pudding was strange, but everyone seemed to be eating normally. I looked at mine again and thought perhaps it wasn't as bad as I had initially thought and took a bit of the apple at the top of the pudding, but as I put it in my mouth, I knew this was a big mistake! Again the taste arrested my taste buds and again I wanted to spit it out, but I had to politely swallow it. I looked at Zoe and by this time she had almost eaten half of her pudding! Ray hadn't started his and two of the others had eaten more than half, when someone at the table said, *"Does anyone else think this pudding is strange?"*

It turned out that everyone was just being polite and we were all wondering what on earth we were eating! We then discovered that one of the catering staff had made a mistake and instead of it being an 'apple something or other', it was an uncooked savoury dish with potatoes, garlic, cloves and herbs and should have been cooked and served as part of a main course! It was just a good job Ray hadn't eaten his as he is allergic to garlic!

TAKE TIME TO
LAUGH, IT'S THE MUSIC
OF YOUR SOUL.

FROM ON OLD ENGLISH PRAYER

HELP!

(A friend called Pam Palmer also decided to share her funny story with me.)

I was 17 years old and wearing my smart red wet look boots and white wet look coat with fake white fur round the hem, cuffs and collar. A group of us were heading off to go bowling. There were road works outside the church, which meant a slight detour to get to our cars. However, I decided I'd take a short cut over the road works! Well, one minute I was there, the next I wasn't! Unbeknown to me, and unseen because it was dark - a 6-foot trench had been dug and I had walked right into it!!

"Help!" I cried, but all I could hear was hysterical laughter up above me. *"I can't get out!"* I shouted. My hysterical friends peered over the top of the trench to see me helpless and hopping on one foot because my ankle had twisted beneath me in the fall! Fortunately someone spotted a ladder and this was placed in the trench and I hopped up to ground level again. Needless to

say, I was very embarrassed, my white coat now looked rather grubby and I had to limp to the car. Somehow I managed to join in a game of 10-pin bowling! I can't remember the score, but that hysterical laughter and embarrassing event will linger in my memory forever as a really funny moment!

LAUGHTER ENHANCES TEAMWORK

Shared laughter is one of the most effective ways of encouraging and enhancing teamwork. Laughter unites people so make sure you include humour in your every day activities.

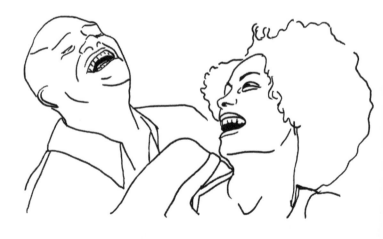

SMILE

Ray and I had just arrived in Johannesburg, South Africa in 1985 after a long flight, so my excuse is that I was very tired. We were then connecting to a domestic flight to Durban. We approached the clerk at the counter and handed him our travel documents. He turned to me and with a smile on his face and said, *"Smile"*. I thought this was a little strange but did my best to send him back a warm and delightful smile. He then asked me again to smile and this time I did an even bigger and full on huge smile! Ray then looked at me with a disturbed look on his face and answered the clerk with *"non smoking please!"* I had not been asked to smile at all, the clerk had only asked me if I wanted the smoking section of the plane and I had not understood his accent. I have to say I felt a little foolish!

LET LOVE AND LAUGHTER
NEVER LEAVE YOU!

WRAP THEM AROUND
YOUR NECK AND TAKE THEM
WHEREVER YOU GO

I FELT LIKE
THE QUEEN

I was speaking at a predominantly black church in London some time back when this funny incident happened. My husband Ray, and friends Esther and Emma were also there with me. I had been getting ready for the service and as I came back I noticed they were speaking to one of the men from the church. Ray told me afterwards that he had told all three of them that 'Pastor Nancy' was to sit on the front row next to the two leaders of the church and they were to sit in the row behind me! I laughed not only at being called 'Pastor Nancy' but also that my husband and two friends had to sit behind me! For a few seconds I felt a little bit like the Queen whose husband always walks a couple of steps behind her. However, I was firmly brought down to earth with a bump when they told me that the man's next question to the three of them was, *"Tell me are you here with your Mum?"* Ray thought this was hilarious and hasn't stopped telling people this story!

LAUGHTER HELPS DEFUSE CONFLICT

There is nothing like laughter that can easily and quickly defuse arguments with others. Laughter can change the atmosphere and mood of those around you.

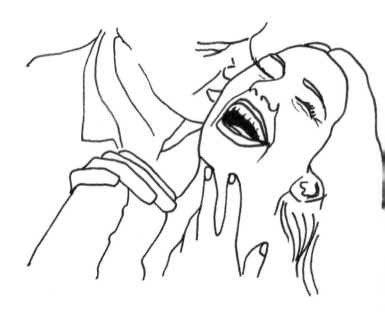

I'M RATHER BUSY
RIGHT NOW!

I saw this funny story on Facebook…

I was in a public toilet and had just sat down, when I heard a voice from the next cubicle. He said, *"Hi, how are you?"*

Embarrassed I said, *"I'm doing fine."*

The voice said, *"So what are you up to?"*

I said, *"The same as you, sitting here!"*

The voice continued, *"Can I come over?"*

Annoyed I said, *"I'm rather busy right now."*

Immediately the voice said, *"Listen, I will have to call you back, there's an idiot next door answering all my questions!"*

CARRY LAUGHTER
WITH YOU WHEREVER
YOU GO

HUGH SIDEY

BURNED ON
THE BUM

When I was a very young child I was wandering around my mum's kitchen with no knickers on (don't ask why – because I have no idea!) when someone pushed me. A few minutes earlier my Mum had just finished the ironing and she had stood the iron upright on the floor waiting for it to cool. When I was pushed, the way I fell I ended up sitting on the point of the hot iron. I had to go to hospital with a burnt bum and back passage! It wasn't funny then, only hugely painful and embarrassing, but I can look back now and laugh!

LAUGHTER PROMOTES GROUP BONDING!

Laughter is a universal language. No matter what people group, race or culture you belong to, the language of laughter is always understood. Laughter has a wonderful way of connecting us with others. No matter what differences we may have when we find something funny, we all respond in the same way – we laugh! When laughter is shared it binds people together and promotes group bonding.

TWO SCOTTISH GENTLEMEN

As an elderly gentleman in a Scottish church stood to address the congregation about an experience he had the previous day, he said, *"Yesterday I had intercourse on the factory floor with a young girl!"* What the gentleman meant by 'intercourse' was that he had been having a conversation, but of course all the young people in the church were under their chairs in fits of laughter as their imaginations ran wild!

Another gentleman who attended the same church as me when I was a youngster and who had his own business in Scotland called 'Martin's Clothing' was trying to attract more people into his shop. So he decided to have a sale and put a huge sign in his window which said, 'Martin's trousers down again!' When we left the church we always had to drive past his shop to get home. This sign and many others in his shop window were always a source of much laughter to everyone in our car!

HOLDING ON TO ANGER,
RESENTMENT AND HURT
ONLY GIVES YOU TENSE
MUSCLES, A HEADACHE
AND A SORE JAW FROM
CLENCHING YOUR TEETH.
FORGIVENESS GIVES YOU
BACK THE LAUGHTER AND
LIGHTNESS IN YOUR LIFE

JOAN LUNDEN

STRONG AND PAINFUL
CONTRACTIONS

I didn't know quite what to expect when it came time for me to deliver my first child. To begin with I was able to deal with the contractions but as the time progressed and the pain increased I remember clearly and distinctly telling Ray, *"That's it! I've had enough. Please take me home now!"* In my pain, I couldn't understand why he wouldn't do that! He and the midwife thought it was funny but needless to say - I did not!

Sometime later a friend of mine became pregnant and the time came for her to deliver her child. She was having severe contractions and her husband was helping her as much as he could by encouraging her to hold on to his hand and telling her it would all soon be over. When a really bad contraction came, she reached out for his hand but instead found his throat and squeezed it really hard. He couldn't get her to let go until the contraction had passed. It wasn't funny at the time, but they did laugh afterwards when she realised that she had almost choked him!

LAUGHTER GIVES US STRENGTH

Nehemiah 8:10 tells us that the joy of the Lord is your strength. There is no doubt that laughter gives us physical strength and energy, but it can also strengthen us spiritually too and make us more aware of the author of the gift of laughter.

"EXCUSE ME SIR"

(A male friend gave me permission to use this story!)

I walked into a local chemist today and asked the lady behind the counter if I could have some cortisone cream. She asked me what it was for and in a quiet embarrassed voice I said, *"It's for a saddle sore."* She asked the chemist and he handed over the tube. She turned to me and said *"That will be £2.99."* I was thinking to myself that I got away well with that. However, as I turned to leave, the chemist shouted out in front of all the customers, *"Excuse me sir, but please make sure you don't put it near your genital area."*

WITH THE FEARFUL
STRAIN THAT IS ON ME
NIGHT AND DAY,
IF I DID NOT LAUGH
I SHOULD DIE.

ABRAHAM LINCOLN

WHERE'S MY MEAL?

Ray and I went into a large hotel in London recently for a meal. We discovered it had a very trendy bar with a large bar menu and so we were looking forward to a nice meal. I ordered a chicken salad and Ray decided to have a steak (both were from the main meals menu) and we also asked for French fries to share. My salad arrived and then the French fries came not too long after. I waited for Ray's steak to come but when it didn't arrive, we called the waitress over and asked her if Ray's meal had been forgotten.

She calmly said, *"Oh, but you didn't order them to come together?"*

I replied, *"But we ordered both meals at the same time."*

She said, *"Yes but you didn't say you wanted the two meals to be served at the same time!"*

I was stunned! I then asked, *"When a couple order their*

meals at the same time, don't you normally bring their main meals together?"

It was only then that she apologised and brought Ray's meal! It was very strange! I thought it must be a wind up and that someone somewhere was perhaps recording us for Candid Camera! But no! It was just a strange situation that made us laugh!

LAUGHTER - YOU BECOME LIKE A LITTLE CHILD (MATT 18:3).

Children laugh so quickly and easily. We are told that the average child laughs around 300 times a day whereas an adult laughs only around four times a day! We all know that children can teach so much about love, acceptance, trust and forgiveness. Let's become like little children and decide to laugh a lot more often!

NEED AN EYE TEST?

(Another friend has allowed me to use her story!)

"I was extremely amused one day when my husband told me this story. One day he had to get his eyes tested so he took himself to the optometrist. He had been wearing glasses for years and needed to check out the strength of his prescription. So he walked into the optometrist that he had been going to for many years and told the lady at the counter he was there for his eye test. The lady at the counter then starts to laugh and states that she definitely thinks he needs to see the eye doctor as soon as possible as he was currently standing in the jewellers. The optometrist was next door!"

IT'S GOOD
TO LAUGH

THE MIDDLE
TOILET

A number of years ago I went to the Evangelical Alliance in London to meet a well-known national speaker. He and I had been asked to speak together at a conference and so we were meeting to discuss what we would say. When I arrived I was told that my partner in crime had already checked in so I decided to go to the loo before meeting him. There are three toilets at the Evangelical Alliance and I chose to go to the middle one. I started to open the door and it seemed a little stuck so I pushed it hard and the door opened to reveal the person I was to meet. He was sitting on the loo with his trousers around his feet reading a newspaper!

LAUGHTER KEEPS YOU GOING IN VERY DIFFICULT CIRCUMSTANCES

(Hebrews 12:2). Laughter is the companion you want to keep with you always, through good and bad situations. When my husband went through emotional burnout, the only people he could see socially were people who caused him to laugh!

ENTHUSIASTIC ORGANIST

Ray my husband and his family attended a Baptist church in Scotland when he was a teenager. In those days, Ray does not remember a lot of laughter within the church, however one day that all changed! Someone in the church was being baptised and so they filled the large baptismal pool, which was just beside where the church organist played the hymns. The hymns at a baptism are very lively and the organist was really playing them with lots of enthusiasm so much so that in the middle of one of the songs, he and the organ stool promptly fell into the baptismal pool! This was all the more funny for Ray, because the organist was his head teacher!

THERE IS NOTHING IN THE
WORLD SO IRRESISTIBLY
CONTAGIOUS AS LAUGHTER
AND GOOD HUMOUR.

CHARLES DICKENS —
A CHRISTMAS CAROL

SPRING INTO LIFE?

My friend, Sherry Gorman-Rickard has given me permission to use her story!

I was bringing a friend along to a meeting called 'Spring into Life' which was being held in a house that I had only visited once a few years previously. I rang the bell of a beautiful Edwardian house and an elderly gentleman answered. I asked *"Spring into Life?"* just to check I had the right house.

He quickly replied, *"Yes!"* He opened the door wide and took us to a room in the house where several elderly ladies were sitting. They welcomed us with a cup of tea, but all the time I was thinking, *"Where are all the younger people?"*

As I sipped my tea, I asked the ladies, *"How long have you been involved with 'Spring into Life'?"*

"What's that?" came the reply from one of the ladies!

I briefly told those who were listening about 'Spring into Life' and they all looked at one another and said, *"Oh, we haven't been involved with that before"*.

I said, *"Oh that's nice! You're new to it then?"* They asked me again to explain it to everyone, which I did.

"Sounds very interesting," they said.

It was at this point that the lady who owned the house said, *"I think you may have the wrong house!"*

My friend and I were sitting in the wrong house! The house we should have been in was a little further up the same street. Embarrassed we thanked them for the tea and quickly left with a funny story to tell the people we were meant to be meeting!

LAUGHTER DISPELS YOUR FEARS FOR THE FUTURE

Proverbs 31:25 tells us we can laugh at things to come. So when life is tough, draw from the strength you have and use laughter to infuse the hope within. Fear cannot live where hope is planted.

WEDDING LAUGHTER

My husband, Ray was asked to speak at a wedding a few years back and decided to tell a joke that he had heard recently. At the same time he decided to personalise it and tell them that Ray and I had been married almost 40 years and that we had sex almost every night of the week. He then added – almost on a Monday, almost on a Tuesday, almost on a Wednesday etc! The audience laughed but the bride's mother didn't get the joke. She was astonished and thought that Ray meant that he and I had sex every night! She had been counselling several married women in her church and decided to go back and tell them about this amazing couple who had been married for many years and still had sex every night! She was encouraging them to learn from our example! It was a few weeks later when she finally got the joke! Someone else who had been at the wedding simply explained that the joke was that they 'almost' had sex every night!

LAUGHTER IS A
TRANQUILIZER WITH
NO SIDE EFFECTS.

ARNOLD GLASOW

ARE YOU COOL?

My husband read an article in the newspaper that was entitled, 'Out of touch with your kids?' and decided to test me on this! He told me that the newspaper had listed several things that make parents uncool. I regard myself as someone who is very much in touch with the youth of today so I thought I would do very well until he said the first statement.

1. Not knowing what is no. 1 in the charts. *(I hadn't a clue!)*

2. Not knowing the words to current songs in the charts. *(Ray has always struggled with the words to songs – even if he has written them, but how can I know the words of songs in the charts if I haven't heard the songs!)*

3. Not seeing the attractions in computer games – *(what is the attraction – does anyone know?)*

4. Not knowing how to work the TV/DVD player. *(I know how to work the TV but the DVD player is beyond me!!)*

5. Not knowing what twerking is! *(When Ray asked me this – I said "Pardon – what was that word you said?")*

6. Not knowing what Spotify is. *(I said "I know what that is – isn't that the name for the app that does photographs?" – Ray laughed loudly)*

7. Boasting about children on Facebook. *(Guilty!!!)*

8. Getting on well with your children's friends. *(I do get on well with my children's friends but what's wrong with that?)*

9. Not knowing who Harry Styles is. *(I excitedly blurted out – "Oh yes I know who this is – isn't he a comedian?" As Ray burst out laughing I got the distinct impression I was wrong! Then I remembered he was the good-looking guy in 'One Direction' – you see I did get there in the end!)*

10. Being a smoker. *(I'm not a smoker – I got therefore one and a half our of ten – do you think I can still say I'm cool? – ha!)*

LAUGHTER CONQUERS THE IMPOSSIBLE AND ENABLES YOU TO SEE BEYOND

Laughing with God means seeing things from a different perspective and this always leads to faith.

THE HEADLIGHTS

A friend, called Heather Gerard, told me this story...

I was driving home and spotted my car mechanic so stopped for a quick chat. When I said goodbye he misheard me and thought that I had said that I needed to go and sort out the headlights.

"I can come over now and have a look," he said.

"Oh no, it's ok, I can do it," I replied.

"Is it both of them?" He asked.

"Yes, unfortunately."

"You know it's illegal."

"No it's not illegal Paul, the school can only request that you keep your children at home but they can't enforce it."

"What's the school got to do with your headlights?" he asked.

"Not headlights Paul, head lice! The children have both got head lice!"

YOU CAN HAVE
AS MUCH LAUGHTER AS
YOU HAVE FAITH

MARTIN LUTHER

EPILOGUE

I read recently about a nurse who had compiled a list of the top five regrets people have when they have come to the very end of their lives. Among them was, *"I wish I had let myself be happier."* At the end of life, no one had a regret that they wished they had experienced more sex, work, or exciting bungee jumps, but one regret many had was that they hadn't laughed more. The nurse recorded that, *"Many did not realise until the end that happiness was a choice. They had stuck to their old patterns and habits. The so-called 'comfort' of familiarity overflowed into their emotions, as well as their physical lives. Fear of change had them pretending to others and to themselves that they were content, when deep within, they longed to laugh properly and have silliness in their life again."* Let's not forget to learn from children around us and laugh often!

Man-made traditions and restraints often mean that we cannot be ourselves or even behave the way we were created to be. If you take the subject of church for instance, tradition has often told us that church is a place that should be solemn and quiet. Isn't it funny how at weddings when we arrive at the reception to have the meal and then dance, the place is full of fun and laughter, but when we go to the church beforehand, many people feel they cannot laugh or express joy of any kind? The impression many people have is that we should be solemn and quiet in church.

When my husband and I were in the band Heartbeat (the band we founded in the 80's) we were asked to play at a huge well-known cathedral in the north of England. As we set up our equipment, we were talking and laughing with each other when an official from the church ran up to us shouting, *"Stop it! Stop it! We don't laugh in this church!"* More's the pity we wanted to say! Maybe if there was more laughter in church many more people would attend!

As I said at the beginning of this book, I believe that God is a happy God. It says in the Bible that he made human beings in his image and if this is correct, then surely God who created us with the ability to laugh would be a God who laughs! The God I believe in is not a God who is always in a bad mood, instead he is a loving, kind and joyful God. From before the world began he loved us and chose us. Every day he blesses us even when we don't realise it. He wants his amazing creation that he loves immensely to be happy, fulfilled and filled with joy. Therefore, church should definitely be a place of joy and celebration!

Good friends of mine had just taken over the leadership of a church in the UK when they discovered that the worship in that particular church was rather doleful and dreary. They asked the worship team if they could include some songs of joy and celebration into their repertoire. The answer they gave was this: *"We don't do joy in this church!"*

WOULD JESUS HAVE LAUGHED?

Someone once remarked to me, *"Jesus would never have laughed! He was holy and solemn and would never ever have laughed!"* Yet if Jesus was the son of God, then why would he not use a gift that his Father had given him and every other human being? As I said earlier, I believe that God created us with the ability to laugh and if you have read earlier what laughter does you have to agree that it really is an incredible gift. Jesus became human just like us, therefore it stands to reason that at points throughout his life he would have laughed.

Have you ever tried to celebrate without laughter? You cannot truly rejoice and celebrate without laughter. Jesus went to many parties and weddings and the criteria of a good party or wedding is that there is much joy and laughter! If a party, a wedding or something similar is planned, then laughter will always be an ingredient that is essential. Jesus said that he came to bring 'life to the full'; I cannot imagine life to the full without having fun, laughter and joy. Can you?

He spoke so much about joy and encouraged those around him to rejoice even in difficult circumstances. Certainly the Bible talks about Jesus being a 'man of sorrows' and certainly he faced many sorrows throughout his 30 plus years of being on this earth, but he encouraged his followers to follow the pathway of joy when facing problems and difficulties. It says in Hebrews 12:2 that when he faced the barbaric death of dying on a cross, it was because of the joy before him that he endured the pain and the suffering. His joy was knowing that everyone could now experience a joy filled life! There is obviously a time to laugh and a time to weep, a time to dance and a time to mourn, as it says in Ecclesiastes 3:4. All these emotions are right and appropriate at various times throughout our lives, but let's not miss out on the times when it is right to choose and focus on joy and laughter.

So laugh a lot, rejoice and don't get to the end of your life and have regrets about not laughing enough. Allow laughter to have a prominent place in your life. We all need to learn from little children who laugh so freely and so often. Fill your life with joy and happiness and...

Nancy Goudie's
Spiritual Health Weekends

THREE EXCITING DAYS TO TRANSFORM YOUR SPIRITUAL WALK

Would you like to be pampered physically and toned up spiritually? Nancy Goudie's Spiritual Health Weekends could be just the thing you are looking for!

Nancy Goudie runs weekend conferences at the end of January and the beginning of February each year at luxury four-star Marriott Hotels in Preston and Bristol. These weekends are for ladies of all ages. Come and enjoy the excellent food, the superb leisure facilities *(spa, steam room, sauna, fitness room and luxury pool)*, the life changing sessions from Nancy, the magnificent banquet and 5 star entertainment and the free pamper treatments plus so much more. Each conference is usually booked well in advance so please book early to avoid disappointment.

This is a women's conference like no other!

FOR MORE INFORMATION AND BOOKING DETAILS CONTACT:

Zoe Wickham at   Tel: 01454 414880
ngm, Caedmon Complex,   Fax: 01454 414812
Bristol Road, Thornbury,   Email: zoewickham@ngm.org.uk
Bristol, BS35 3JA.   Or visit: www.nancygoudie.com

OTHER BOOKS AND PRODUCTS

BY NANCY GOUDIE

The Beloved - *£5.00 (hardback book)*
This is a collection of real stories, poems, wise words, meditations and huge encouragement to know that you are immensely loved! Any time you are feeling down, unloved, criticised or critical of yourself and life hits you hard, then pick up this book and flick through its pages. Each page is designed to bring you words of encouragement, hope and love.

This book can be purchased by visiting www.nancygoudie.com or www.ngm.org.uk/shop or by calling 01454 414880.

Confident? - *£5.00 (hardback book)*

This book is for anyone who sometimes swings from being confident to feeling a failure. It's a book full of encouragement, wise words, poems, songs and stories to lift your spirit and get you back on your feet again, ready to face life once more. Through its pages you will feel accepted, really loved and realise afresh how amazing you are!

This book can be purchased by visiting www.nancygoudie.com or www.ngm.org.uk/shop or by calling 01454 414880.

You are Special - *£5.00 (hardback book)*
In our culture of stress with so much
pressure to look good and be famous, we
often need to be reminded just how unique,
precious, remarkable and extraordinary we
are! No matter what colour our skin is, what
size we are, what intelligence we display,
what background we come from, the truth is
each of us is an exceptional human being. In
every page of this book you will discover the
truth about yourself and realise afresh that
you are deeply loved, special and accepted.

*This book can be purchased by visiting
www.nancygoudie.com or www.ngm.org.uk/shop
or by calling 01454 414880.*

MEDITATION CD

Peace Like a River - *£8.00*
If you have ever experienced stress, carried worries, fought fears or are just looking for an oasis in your busy life, then this CD is for you. This recording will take you to a place of tranquillity where peace, love and grace are yours in abundance. Use this CD daily and you will find peace like a river flowing through your soul.

This CD can be purchased direct by visiting
www.nancygoudie.com or www.ngm.org.uk/shop
or by calling 01454 414880.

MEDITATION CD

Smile - *£8.00*
If you are feeling the daily stresses of life, the busyness of work, the pressures of family or just need some soothing for your soul, then this recording is for you.

This CD can be purchased direct by visiting www.nancygoudie.com or www.ngm.org.uk/shop or by calling 01454 414880.

ABOUT THE AUTHOR

Nancy Goudie is a well known author and speaker. She and her husband Ray lead New Generation Music based at Caedmon, their state of the art music complex in Thornbury, Bristol, England. Nancy has written 13 books and 5 meditation CD's, produces her own yearly Spiritual Health magazine and also runs unique and popular Spiritual Health Weekends in luxury hotels. Hundreds of ladies of all ages from all over the UK and beyond travel each year to Bristol and Preston to attend these conferences. Nancy is a qualified public speaker and is often heard on Radio and TV. Nancy and Ray have two sons, Daniel and Aidan.

Should you wish to contact Nancy
then do write to her at:

ngm,
Caedmon Complex,
Bristol Road,
Thornbury,
Bristol, BS35 3JA,
England.

Phone: 01454 414880
Fax: 01454 414812
Email: nancy@nancygoudie.com
Website: www.nancygoudie.com

Like Nancy Goudie page on **facebook**.
(www.facebook.com/nancygoudie)

Follow Nancy on **twitter** *(@nancygoudie)*

Join the *'Nancy Goudie's Spiritual Health Weekends'*
group on **facebook**.